AIRFIX
magazine guide 26

American Tanks
of
World War 2

Terry Gander and Peter Chamberlain

Patrick Stephens Ltd
in association with Airfix Products Ltd

First published—1977

ISBN 0 85059 260 7

Cover design by Tim McPhee

Text set in 8 on 9 pt Univers Medium by Stevenage Printing Limited, Stevenage.
Printed in Great Britain on Fineblade cartridge 90 gsm and bound by the Garden City Press, Letchworth, Herts.
Published by Patrick Stephens Limited, Bar Hill, Cambridge, CB3 8EL, in association with Airfix Products Limited, London SW18.

Don't forget these other Airfix Magazine Guides!

Contents

Editor's introduction

This book is the final title in a series of four covering the major tanks and armoured fighting vehicles of the 'big four' during the last war — America, Britain, Germany and Russia, all of which combine detailed historical information with hard data, scale plans and photographs of the various vehicles described.

During World War 2 America became the 'arsenal of civilisation', and nowhere is this better reflected than in the fact that American industry between 1940 and 1945 succeeded in manufacturing nearly double the quantity of tanks produced by Britain and Germany combined. American tanks were not the best in the world by a considerable margin, but what they lacked in quality they more than made up for in quantity. It is fair to say that without the ubiquitous Sherman we would not have won the war, and this vehicle must certainly enter the annals of history as one of the decisive weapons of all time.

American tank design was hampered — as in Britain — in the early days by the hoary old infantry support controversy, which resulted in a dearth of viable designs and a host of experimental monsters. In a remarkably short space of time, however, a rapid sequence of useful vehicles was produced: the light M3 and M5 Stuarts (or 'Honeys'); the medium M3 Lee and Grant, which gave the embattled British 8th Army in the desert parity with German armour for the first time; the various marks and variants of Sherman; and, at the end of the war, a fine light tank, the M24 Chaffee, and an excellent heavy, the M26 Pershing.

This book describes in concise detail the development stages of each of these vehicles and the modifications which were later made to them in the light of field requirements. Four-view plans are included, as well as data tables on representative vehicles, notes on American tank armament, and a useful chapter for modellers on US AFV camouflage and markings. Combine these attributes with the many marvellous photographs from Peter Chamberlain's extensive collection, and the end result is an invaluable and inexpensive reference source for all military historians and enthusiasts, modellers and wargamers.

BRUCE QUARRIE

one

Tank development up to 1940

During the Great War, up till 1917, the United States of America stood aloof from the events happening in Europe. The armed forces, such as they were, only sent a few observers to comment on the course of the war and from what happened later it would seem that what little intelligence they sent back was disregarded or neglected. But in 1917 the sinking of the *Lusitania*, combined with the German declaration of unrestricted submarine warfare, forced the hand of the American body politic and the USA went to war. However, America at this time was woefully unprepared for warfare on the modern scale. The US Army had a small regular nucleus but it was very much a garrison army, even if the US Cavalry was one of the finest cavalry formations still in existence. The cavalry was well-trained

and had a tradition based on the protracted Plains fighting that conquered the Old West, but it had no place on the battlefields of Europe.

The rest of the US Army was no better off. There were few guns, virtually no heavy artillery, little modern transport and the small-arms industry was not geared to the demands of the Great War, even though many American firms had been making armaments for various European combatants. But the USA did have two major assets. These were men and the industrial capacity of the richest nation in the world. The men flocked to the recruiting booths, but in the long run it was the industrial might of America that made the greatest contribution to the eventual Allied victory.

However, in 1917 that industrial strength was not ready to be used. It took massive efforts to get the factories which were geared to the needs of peace ready to supply the requirements of modern war. As a general rule, the new American armies were short of everything from uniforms to rifles, machine-guns and artillery. When the newly recruited armies landed in Europe they had to take whatever their French and British allies could offer

Ford 3-ton tank.

them, and the major contribution came from the French.

By the time the Americans arrived, a new weapon was making its presence felt: the tank.

Although a handful of far-sighted tacticians saw the potential of the tank in warfare, few were able to see it as more than a possible means of breaking the trench warfare stalemate that had become a virtual fixture by 1918. The American military hierachy was no better and no worse than other national military staffs in this area, but it soon became obvious to the Americans that there was a need for tanks, and lots of them if they were going to take any major part in the war. Orders went back to the States for tanks, but in the meantime the American armies in

American Tanks of World War 2

Europe took over numbers of British and French vehicles—these were mainly the little French Renault FT17 and the British Mark IV and V. The Renault tank was one of those selected for manufacture in the USA and production lines were set up to make the large numbers needed. The British Mark VI was also selected for production, but none were actually made, as by early 1918 the joint British-American-French staff decided that a new tank, the Mark VIII would be built.

Despite the massive production potential of the USA it soon became obvious that factories took a long time to convert to the needs of war, and the tank was only one weapon which was needed in large numbers. Arsenals were set up to produce artillery and similar weapons, the automobile factories were busy turning out lorries, and all major industries were working up to a high pitch to turn out the thousand and one essential items needed by a modern army. Although tanks were given a high priority, time slipped by as production lines were assembled. The time lag involved is difficult to understand as the caterpillar track was an established product in the USA. Indeed, a few American tank projects had been designed by 1917, most of them being agricultural tractors covered in armour plate. A few, such as the Studebaker Supply Tank and the little Ford 3-Ton Tank, took some note of design trends in Europe and were

selected for production, but the two main types were the French Renault and the Mark VIII.

The French tank was known to the Americans as the M1917—this was the American production version as opposed to those taken over from the French which were known as the Renault FT Light Tank. The M1917 was built to American production standards and differed in several respects from the French original. Being a relatively small vehicle this tank could be turned out more easily than larger varieties and as a result they were the only American tanks to arrive in France before the end of 1918—ten were delivered just after the Armistice of November 1918 was signed. But these were the forerunners of a mighty host, for back in the USA the time lag caused by getting tanks into production was over and the industrial might of American factories was ready to churn out tanks by the thousand. One of these, the little Ford 3-Ton Tank, was a typical American example of using the experience gained in the mass production of motor vehicles to adapt to the needs of the military. The Ford tank used many automobile components and it was intended for use as a machine-gun carrier, a tractor or as an ammunition carrier. It had a two-man crew and after troop trials in France in late 1918 it was selected for production. Such was the mass production might of the Ford company that it was able to take orders

for no fewer than 15,000 3-Ton tanks, but the Armistice led to this order being cancelled and only 15 were built.

Much the same happened to the Mark VIII. A great deal of effort and experience went into setting up the lines for these large tanks, not only for the tanks themselves but for their engines. The main assembly lines were to have been in France, but there were numerous delays, mainly caused by material shortages, and the war ended before real production could start. Thus the American Mark VIII, or 'Liberty', was produced in small numbers only (about 100) and it formed the main part of the American tank park until 1932. There they were joined by the M1917—some 950 of which were produced after the Armistice — and again massive production runs which had been planned were cancelled.

The US Army ended the war with a sizeable tank potential which would have done much to tip the scales still further in the Allies' favour had the war continued into 1919. As it was, this potential was not realised to anything like its full extent, for tanks are only machines used by men, and it is still how they use them rather than what they are that determines the course of battles. It was this use of tanks that was the shortfall of the post-war American Army. Relatively few American soldiers were able to gain any experience of the tank in warfare and what little they did obtain was limited to the unique nature of the Western Front terrain. A US Tank Corps was set up by the end of 1917 with a large planned establish-

ment, but by the end of 1918 only three battalions had seen any action and one other battalion was just able to see action before the Armistice.

Soon after the war ended the huge production contracts were cancelled and the newly formed Tank Corps was officially disbanded in 1920. The small nucleus of a modern tank force was scattered and thus unable to make itself heard as the US Army settled down to a 'normal' peace-time existence, and the military mind went back to the world of pre-1914 when the horse was the supreme war animal. The love of the horse is understandable when one considers the lore and traditions of the Old West and the US Cavalry, but many officers in the US military hierarchy had little or no experience of the tank in Europe and like so many others elsewhere tended to regard the tank as a unique 'gimmick' suitable only for the conditions of the Western Front with little or no tactical potential. As late as 1941 some influential American military journals were still stating that the horse had a place in modern warfare, but this dislike of the modern fighting vehicle was taken further than most other armies, for in 1920 the disbandment of the Tank Corps was coupled with an edict that thenceforth tanks were to be used only in support of infantry.

However, there were officers in the American Army who had gained tank experience in France in 1918 and these few fought an uphill battle to develop new equipment and tactics. On the tactical side their gains were few, despite the short-lived formation of a

American Tanks of World War 2

Left *6-ton tanks (M1917) in service with the Canadian Army* **Right** *Mark VIII Liberty Tanks waiting to be handed over to the Canadian Army.*

'Mechanised Force' similar in concept and formation to the British Experimental Mechanised Force. This eventually died under the weight of the US Army's inherent conservatism and financial straits, as did the British experiment when it ran into the demands of the British Treasury.

On the equipment side there were very few results to show. From 1920 until 1935 only 35 new tanks were produced. Every one of them was virtually hand-made and almost all of them were designed and built with some special concept in mind. This is not to say that these designs were of little value, although as fighting tanks most of them left much to be desired. These few tank designs tried out many of the features that were later to become part of the philosophy of American tank designs after 1941. Indeed, one of the designs based on the experimental work of J. Walter Christie had a great impact on later tank development, but it was an odd quirk of fate that the excellent tank suspension developed by an American inventor was only used on prototype American vehicles and went on to be adopted overseas on tanks like the Russian T-34 series and British vehicles such as the Crusader. In fact, the Christie 'story' is an odd side-alley that contributed little to the main tale of American tank development between the wars. However, a few designs were produced for the American forces, the most important of which was the Medium Tank T3, later developed into the T4.

By the mid-1930s the American tank arm was weak in numbers and equipment. Its old ex-Great War equipment had passed from use and was stacked away in storage yards. (Many of these old M1917s and Mark VIIIs were dragged out in 1940 and passed over to Canada to form the training nucleus of the Canadian tank arm.) Financial problems were a constant worry so what little tank development that did take place concentrated on small, relatively cheap, light tanks. For a while these light tanks had to use the cover name of 'Combat Cars' as tanks were intended to be the prerogative of the infantry and the US Cavalry were supposed to have no hand in their use.

By 1935 the tank protagonists were making ground against the diehard horse faction, and small numbers of light tanks were gradually being infused into cavalry formations. At first the numbers were small and the equipment, to put it mildly, was not very impressive. The Light Tank T1 series were all virtually 'one-off' vehicles that were slow and not very reliable, but with the T2 series—later the Light Tank M2—a much more viable vehicle emerged.

When the M2A4 emerged in the late 1930s the division of the infantry and cavalry responsibilities had vanished, and the US Army was gradually compiling a useful backlog of tank experience. The horse was at long last giving way to the internal combustion engine, and with their light tanks the Americans were in some ways ahead of tank design elsewhere, especially in armament. While other nations were still equipping their light tanks with machine-guns, the M2A4 had a 37 mm gun. It was also larger than most contemporary light tanks, but its size was also one of its weaknesses as it was largely constructed from riveted plates which time was to show would be a disadvantage in battle. This method of construction was dictated by the lack of any other manufacturing method, and it was here that the American tank programme was already way behind the rest of the world.

By the late 1930s the war clouds were once more gathering over Europe. Nations once more began to plan armament production on a large scale even if the actual hardware was still not in evidence. But in the USA the huge war production machine, that had been so frantically built up at great cost in 1917 and 1918, had almost as quickly been dismantled and American industry went back peacefully to producing motor cars and the needs of the consumer industries. The days of the Great Depression of the late 1920s and early 1930s were hardly condusive to armament production, especially as the USA seemed set for a long period of peaceful neutrality. The USA stood aloof from the events of Europe and was therefore not able to sense the coming catastrophe. While the US Army gradually worked out its future tactics with handfuls of light tanks, the German Army began to organise its Panzer divisions and set up the industrial background to produce large numbers of heavy tanks. But in the USA tank production plans were under the aegis of the Ordnance Board, a body more used to producing guns than vehicles, and understandably they had little idea of how far their tank design and production plans were falling behind the rest of the world. However, as stated above, by 1939 they had a good light tank design that embodied many fine features, several of which were later to be embodied into larger medium tanks. Perhaps the most important feature was the vertical volute (coiled spring) suspension that was later to be enlarged to suit the Lee/Grant and Sherman medium tanks. Also, during the early war years at least, a tank was of little use without a viable armament and the M2A4 had a 37 mm gun. Reliability was an ever-increasing factor in engine design, but as late as 1940 no plans were ready for the mass-production of engines, nor indeed for any major armaments in the USA.

But some progress had been made. A few small 'tank education' contracts had been put out to industry to get them used to the needs of tank production; there had been some trials with cast and welded armour and the first tentative plans had been made for considering the needs of modern warfare. Things were moving gradually.

two

Tank development 1940-1945

1940 was to be the watershed of American tank development and production. The events of late 1939 had been observed with a great deal of interest, much of it officially academic, as the US government was still geared to remaining neutral from the war in Europe. However, many Americans realised that they could not remain detached from the course of events, and planned accordingly. Also, the nations of Europe, other than Germany, were in no better shape regarding modern equipment than were the Americans, and they began to place armament orders with American industry. The economy of the USA was on an upsurge and production of all types was booming.

At long last production plans for tanks were made and placed into the realms of large orders. Most of these orders were for light tanks but the first sizeable orders for medium tanks were also issued. The vehicle chosen for the early orders was the Medium Tank M2, the result of a development programme that began with Medium Tank T5 of 1938. This tank was an enlarged Light Tank M2 that was intended for use in support of infantry. To this end it bristled with no fewer than eight machine-guns and even had such items as deflector plates to guide machine-gun fire down into trenches. Its main armament was a 37 mm gun and it used an air-cooled radial aircraft engine. A later version was selected for mass production, the M2A1, which had thicker armour. Contracts were placed with two locomotive manufacturing plants as it was thought that not only

did they have the right kind of plant and machinery to make tanks but at that time they also had spare capacity. Engine contracts were also placed, not only for the air-cooled aircraft engine but also for diesel engines.

During 1940 these plans were put into the melting pot. The early plans were soon found to be far too small-scale. The US Army was already envisaging that it would have to play a major part in World War 2 and wanted to get modern equipment as quickly as possible. France and the United Kingdom were both beginning to order military equipment on a major scale and tanks were high on the list of priorities of these customers. It soon became apparent that not even American industry would be able to meet the forthcoming needs without a major expansion, so this was planned.

Early plans called for production rates of 1,741 medium tanks to be built over 18 months but this was soon seen as being too conservative. It was not long before production rates of ten tanks a day were being spoken of, ie well over twice the original rate. The problem was solved in what was to become a typical American way. It was passed over to the production engineers of the automobile industry at Detroit, the heart of the American car industry. Armed with plans of the M2A1 they took less than a month to plan and design a new tank arsenal to be built just outside Detroit. The new plant, to become known as the Detroit Tank Arsenal, was to cost $21,000,000 and was to turn out the required ten tanks a day. To back up the output of this arsenal the firms already tooling up to produce tanks would expand their lines and new firms were to be included in the programme. The arsenal plans were given the go-ahead and the new buildings started to grow on a 100-acre plot of farmland just outside the city. At the same time the machine tooling, jigs and labour needed for M2A1 production were swiftly organised.

All this frantic activity took place in June and July of 1940, but much of it was already misdirected. During May 1940 the German Panzer divisions had swept all before them in France and one swift lesson from that campaign was that German tank armament was already at a more advanced stage than the Americans had envisaged. The German PzKpfw IV was armed with a 75 mm gun so any future American tank had to have parity at least. The Detroit Arsenal was gearing up for a tank armed with a mere 37 mm gun so all the plans were put into the melting pot and the M2A1 was destined never to be produced in quantity. Instead its hull and chassis were used as the basis for a new design, the M3. The Medium Tank M3 was intended only as a stop-gap design until a fresh design with a 75 mm gun in a 360° traverse turret could be produced. The stop-gap M3 did have a 75 mm gun but it was placed in a hull sponson with a very limited traverse. A new cast turret with a 37 mm gun was placed on top of the hull. This new design was produced in a very short time — even the gun was a hasty revision as it was a much-altered weapon based on the old French '75' of World War 1. Plans at the new arsenal, then still being built, were drastically revised and new machines and jigs hastily assembled but even then it was

not until April 1941 that the first M3 ran off the still-new assembly line. Considering the fact that the production engineers were planning to produce tanks that had yet to be designed, in a factory which was yet to be built, at a time when actual numbers had yet to be determined, the medium tank production story must rank as one of the finest achievements of American industry to that date. It was done at great cost and with a massive diversion of labour and materials but it must not be forgotten that it was carried out at a time when the whole spectrum of American industry was in a state of flux.

During 1940 the industrial scope of America was changing and expanding rapidly. Aviation, electrical, optical, shipping, lorries, chemical — all industry was in a state of change, a change that had largely been unplanned and unforeseen. The Tank Arsenal and the tank programme was but one section of this expansion and as a result the problems were legion. High on the list was machine tools of all kinds. Every facet of industry was crying out for them during 1940 (and after) and in 1940 the top priorities went to

American Tanks of World War 2

the aircraft and other industries. As a result there were several bottlenecks in tank production. Another arose from the fact that aircraft engines had been selected for a sizeable portion of the M3 series, and not surprisingly these same engines were needed for aircraft — especially training aircraft. A further bottleneck came with engine transmissions and final drives. This latter problem had one odd facet when two plants were about to produce their first production M3s. The first tank from one plant was ceremoniously rolled off the line only for the transmission to be removed and rushed to another plant for fitting in the first M3 off their line!

These problems gradually resolved themselves, however, and the M3 design then began a period of gradual development and change. The early M3s used the conventional riveted plate construction (apart from the cast turret) which was soon proved to be at a disadvantage in action. The flush-sided plates used offered little chance of shot deflection and the rivets had a nasty tendency to fly out when hit. Early M3s also had large doors in the sides which weakened the structure. The engine bottleneck was resolved by a number of means. The Wright Continental aircraft engine was re-placed in a number of M3s by Guiberson diesel engines and a further batch were powered by a remarkable improvisation produced by combining five standard Chrysler engines into the Chrysler A-57 Multibank engine. Another similar improvisation was bought about by combining two General Motors diesel engines. The result was a great number of tanks produced but the problems of maintaining so many types of tank and engine can be imagined.

In the field the M3 was a remarkable success. The first to see action were those delivered to the British. These M3s (renamed the 'Grant' by the British when their own modifications had been made), had been built to a British order issued in 1940 by a purchasing commission. The British M3 had a revised turret to accommodate a radio but they also later received numbers of the standard M3 which they called the 'Lee'. Canada also ordered the M3 and later deliveries were made to Russia. The main attraction for the British was that the M3 was available in potential numbers, but in action in North Africa from 1942 onwards the best feature of the tank was its 75 mm gun. This put the hard-pressed British tank crews on a parity with their German opponents for the first time, but the height of the M3 was a tactical disadvantage, and there were many occasions when the limited traverse of the gun was also a severe limitation. Considering that the M3 was a stop-gap design, it turned out to be a remarkably good one, and what limitations it had were more than overcome by the fact that it was there when needed. By 1944 it was obsolete as a fighting tank and was either scrapped, cannibalised for spares for later tanks, or converted to such mundane roles as armoured recovery vehicle (ARV) or used for training and trials.

Left *Medium Tank M2.* **Right** *Production of Medium Tanks M3 in the Detroit Tank Arsenal.*

Above *M4A1 Medium Tanks in production at the Lima Locomotive Works, Ohio.* **Right** *M3 Medium Tanks on the assembly line.*

At the same time as the M3 was being rushed into production, the light tanks were gradually being produced in greater and greater numbers. Being smaller and lighter vehicles they were more easily produced without major disruption of facilities, but even so it still took time to set up production lines on the scale needed. The M2A4 was gradually developed into the Light Tank M3 which was produced in several versions, most of which reflected the engine bottleneck problem by using a variety of engines. The Light Tank M3 was ordered by the British who used it as the 'Stuart' and it first saw action in North Africa. Compared with contemporary designs, the Light Tank M3 was a large vehicle but one that proved more than adequate when used in the reconnaissance role. Progressive development did away with the early riveted construction, welding took its place, and eventually the Light Tank M3 gave way to the Light Tank M5. This was the last version of the light tanks to see service on a large scale. It was delivered to the British Army (as the Stuart VI), and was modified into a number of special purpose variants.

However, development of the light tank did not stop with the M5. A replacement project for the M3 and M5 was the Light Tank T7. This vehicle was one of the major misjudgements made by the tank development authorities in the USA. On paper the T7 looked a very viable tank and a major production facility was planned for it, known as the Quad Cities Tank Arsenal, at Bettendorf, Iowa. Production plans went ahead on a lavish scale with an eventual planned output of 750 tanks a month. The T7 design was gradually up-gunned from a 37 mm weapon to take a 57 mm gun. Then that too was replaced by a 75 mm gun, by which time the chassis was grossly overloaded and a new engine design was needed. Only 13 T7s were produced before the whole project was run-down at a cost large in money and diversion of effort. None of the T7s saw service.

A more successful light tank was the M22. This was intended as an airborne tank for carrying in large gliders. Relatively few were produced and a quantity were handed over to the British airborne forces who used it during the Rhine Crossings in March 1945.

Although it arrived on the scene almost too late for active service in Europe, the Light Tank M24 was one of the best of the American light tank designs, although at a weight of over 18 tons it was stretching the point to call it a light tank. Armed with a 75 mm gun, the M24 was an exceptionally good vehicle which incorporated a great deal of battle experience in its design concept.

To return to the medium tank scene: almost at the same time as the M3 production line was getting under way, plans were being made for its replacement, the Medium Tank M4. The M4 was to become one of America's greatest contributions to eventual Allied victory as it was produced in thousands. The M4 was intended to overcome the traverse limitations of the M3 by having its 75 mm gun set in a fully traversing turret which could turn through 360°. The hull and chassis were gradual developments of the earlier M2 and M3 components but the

welded construction (which was used on some early M4 versions) gradually gave way to one-piece cast assemblies. The casting of large one-piece armour assemblies was a result of experiments made before 1939. These experiments enabled industry to turn out components that were stronger than conventional assemblies, took less production time and machining, and also produced curved surfaces which were able to deflect anti-tank shot projectiles. The M4 also had thicker armour than the M3 and as time went on the basic M4 design was gradually altered to accommodate the changing needs of warfare. Not only was armour gradually increased but the 75 mm gun was eventually replaced by a more powerful 76 mm gun and some special purpose variants mounted a 105 mm howitzer in the turret.

The changeover from the M3 to the M4 began in June 1942. New tank production plants were set up to churn out the ever-increasing numbers called for, not only for the US forces but also for the still expanding armies of the Allies such as the UK, the Free French, the Canadians and even the Russians. Almost every Allied nation used the M4 at one time or another and such were the numbers produced that the M4 is still in widespread use in 1977.

By the end of 1941 the planned production output of 1,000 tanks was well under way but a sudden presidential decree that this was to be raised to 2,800 a month was then made. This was combined with an increased priority rating and the result was a massive expansion of tank production facilities—to the detriment of other much-needed war material. The tanks were produced but again the M4 programme ran into the perennial engine problem. This complicated production to such an extent that the M4 was being made with five different engines on the various production lines. The problems this caused to the maintenance echelons in the field can be imagined. But the M4s rolled off the lines in increasing numbers and were shipped all over the world. They went into action in North Africa in late 1942 with the British and thereafter were in action wherever the Allies fought. The number of variants were legion and are covered in the section devoted to this topic in the next chapter, but it must not be thought that the M4, or Sherman as the British knew it, was the perfect fighting tank. It was rather high and as time went on it came increasingly up against the German heavy tanks such as the Panther and Tiger. It proved more and more unsuitable when pitted against the powerful German heavies, but despite armour increases and up-gunning, it was all the Allies had. In the end it was not the fighting potential of the M4 that defeated the German Panzer formations but the sheer weight of numbers and material, which combined with the expertise and gallantry of their Allied crews to overwhelm the enemy.

In many ways the sheer bulk of the M4 production lines was detrimental to the Allied efforts. By 1943 the American tank forces were established along the lines of well-balanced armoured divisions which needed the support of mobile artillery and motorised infantry. Gradually the assembly lines turned from tank production to such items as armoured cars (needed for the reconnaissance role), half-tracks for the infantry in a myriad of variants, self-propelled artillery, and by 1944 an increasing number of tank-killer vehicles. These tank-killers were specialised light tracked chassis adapted to carry heavy anti-tank weapons at relatively high speeds. Their role was quite simply the destruction of enemy tanks to enable the conventional tanks to keep their mobility and firepower for the deep armoured thrust. Typical of these tank-killers were the Gun Motor Carriage M10 and Gun Motor Carriage M36, both based on the M4 chassis.

By 1944 the tank production lines began gradually to run down. This released the capacity of the lines to remanufacture early versions of light and medium tanks. This refurbishing operation had been carried on from about 1941 but only on a relatively small scale. By 1944 it was carried out on a large scale and thus many battle scarred M4s were updated, up-armoured, up-gunned and returned to action. Not only ex-battle tanks were so refurbished. Many old vehicles that went along the reassembly lines were tanks that had suffered the harsh riguors involved in extensive training programmes in the USA.

However, by the end of 1944 the demands for increasing numbers of tanks rose again. Once more it was the M4 that formed the bulk of demands but the tank production lines had been gradually run down or switched to other production so it was another long task to convert them. Then, just as things were building up to a new peak, the end of the war in Europe was seen to be near and the demands fell for the

Medium Tanks M4 on the assembly line.

American Tanks of World War 2

last time. Production of the M4 went on until 1946 to fulfill existing contracts by which time well over 40,000 Medium Tank M4s had been constructed. This truly prodigious output was made at terrific cost both in money and manpower — no nation other than the USA could possibly have done it.

Nevertheless, as stated above, the M4 was not a perfect fighting vehicle. Time and again it was pitted against the superior Tiger and Panther and questions were asked as to why the designers had not produced a heavy tank design. The short answer to the question was that a heavy tank design *was* produced as far back as 1941. This was the Heavy Tank M6 which was originally the Heavy Tank T1 designed by the Ordnance Department well before the USA entered the war. The concept ran into a great deal of trouble from politicians who saw no need for such a heavy tank (it weighed over 56 tons and was armed with a 3-inch gun). The project was delayed and small-scale production commenced in 1942. Only a few were actually produced and none saw combat. One of the main problems was shipping space. Two M4s could be shipped to a theatre of action in the space taken by one M6 and the troops in the field preferred the two M4s. By the time the need for heavy tanks became painfully apparent the M6 was no longer available and anyway, it was very much a first attempt. It was under-gunned for its weight and the internal layout proved unsatisfactory so it was used for various trials and development. From these trials emerged the Heavy Tank M26 — the Pershing. This powerful tank was a match for any tank in 1945 as it mounted a 90 mm gun and was reliable and available. By late 1944 it was rolling off the assembly lines in ever-growing numbers but it saw only limited action in Europe before the war ended.

This was not the only heavy tank to see service as there was one other special purpose tank under development in 1944. This was the Assault Tank T14, a heavy, well-armoured version of the Medium Tank M4 intended for the expected assault on the Siegfried Line. In the event the Line was bypassed without the expected difficulty and the T14 did not pass the trials stage. Another heavily armoured tank was the M4A3E2 or 'Jumbo' which was intended for close infantry support. It was produced in some numbers and saw service in North-East Europe.

From the M4 series sprang a multitude of special purpose, experimental and trial vehicles for every conceivable component of tank armament and equipment: mine-clearing vehicles, flamethrower tanks, rocket-firing tanks and such items as self-propelled artillery. Many of these vehicles remained very much 'one-off' examples but there were so many of them a book of this nature quite simply cannot mention them all. Many variants were produced in British service and the reader is recommended to read the *Airfix Magazine Guide* on British tanks of World War 2 (No 17) for their details. Not only the M4 series was so used; the light tanks also ran to a whole range of versions.

American tanks were far from being perfect fighting vehicles but when one considers the lack of a development base that they sprung from they were all truly remarkable tanks. From the little Light Tank M3 up through the Medium Tank M3 to the Medium Tank M4, they were all good, sturdy, reliable vehicles. They were available in large numbers and the generosity of the American nation ensured that they were distributed to all who needed them. Time and again it was this sheer weight of numbers that made the American tanks the war winners they undoubtedly were. A single statistic will give an idea of the scale of the American production effort. Between 1940 and 1945, American industry produced 88,410 tanks. Without those massive numbers the Allies would never have been able to win the war.

three

American tank designations

When the tank entered the American armoury the designation system in use was a simple model number provided by the year of entry into service, eg M1917 for the Renault Light Tank, where the M meant model. This simple system was later replaced by the one in use throughout World War 2, a system which was also basically simple but which requires a little explanation.

The system was designed for use with every single item used by the US Army and was applied to everything from tanks to gun sights, vehicle components and tents. Thus the first part of every designation had to signify exactly what the item was. In the case of tanks this meant Light Tank, Medium Tank or Heavy Tank. Special items such as Assault Tanks were denoted as such.

The second part denoted the exact status of the item. Thus a tank in the experimentation or trials stage was denoted by a letter T (T-test). This was followed by a number issued in chronological order from which it could usually be seen which item was the more modern, eg a Light Tank T2 would be later than a Light Tank T1. When a tank was selected for service the T letter was replaced by the letter M which signified that the vehicle was standardised for service and all drawings relating to that exact model were 'frozen' along with such items as manuals, etc. At first the number was also changed to suit the chronological order of the M series, eg the Medium Tank T5 became the Medium Tank M2, but later, to spare the inevitable confusions, the T number was kept the same when transferred to the M series of numbers, eg the Light Tank T24 became the Light Tank M24.

The system could also accommodate major alterations bought about by operational or equipment changes after standardisation. Such a major variation would often be along the lines of a different type of engine being fitted or a change of important equipment such

M4A1 (76mm) crossing the Belgian border.

Above left *Cargo Carrier M30.* **Above right** *Medium tank M3 with M2 75mm gun.*

as a gun or ammunition stowage. These alterations were denoted by the letter A after the M number, eg Light Tank M2A1. The most obvious user of these A numbers was the Medium Tank M4 which ran to a whole series of them (qv).

A further complication was added by the use of E numbers (E—experimental). Normally these were used in conjunction with T numbers to denote various changes made during trials before standardisation, eg Light Tank T9E1 (later to become the Light Tank M22). These E numbers were not usually kept after standardisation but there were exceptions.

The system worked very well but, as with every designation system, there were snags and exceptions. For instance, a tank crewman listening to an infantryman talking about an M3 might assume he meant the Medium Tank M3 while the infantryman was referring, in fact, to the submachine-gun M3. Another problem was that the numbers tended to become rather complex, eg Medium Tank M4A3E8. Thus the troops in the field came to add their own nicknames, none of which became official but their use was widespread. The M4A3E8 just mentioned became the 'Easy Eight', the Light Tank series were often known as 'Honeys' and the Assault Tank M4A3E2 became the 'Jumbo'.

A further complication came with the introduction of 'substitute standard' vehicles and equipment. This designation was applied to equipment that had been considered obsolete or was of limited value in its role, but could still be considered useful in limited or training areas. This made no practical difference to most designations but 'on paper' they were further designated 'substitute standard', eg Light Tank (Airborne) M22 (limited standard).

Yet more complications came with the introduction of such items as rocket launchers and bulldozer blades, many of which were never issued with M numbers. A good example of this was the rocket launcher T34 which was fitted to many different types of M4. Here the T number was retained as the launcher was classified as a 'limited procurement' item, ie it was intended originally to be used in small numbers only.

To take a collective example to complete this short introduction to the subject, let us consider the Medium Tank M3A2. This medium tank was the third of its type to be standardised, and the A2 depicted the second major change (an all-welded hull) to be introduced since the type was standardised.

four

American tank data

The Light Tanks

Although there had been little enough tank development prior to 1940, what had been carried out had been concentrated on light tanks. The reasons for this were simple, one of the main ones being that an upper weight limit had been put upon tanks of 15 tons—this was purely a bridge loading limit. Another even simpler reason was that there was very little money available for tank development and research and the light tank was a relatively cheap vehicle with which to experiment.

After 1920 there were various trial and experimental vehicles produced, nearly all of them on a simple 'one-off' basis. An Act of 1920 had stated that the tank was to be a purely infantry weapon, but some tank protagonists in the US Cavalry foresaw that their arm would eventually take over the tank role. As they were forbidden to 'own' their own tanks, they developed a number of vehicles under the cover name of Combat Cars. Despite their cover name, these vehicles were really light tanks. They were developed from the infantry tanks and were quite similar to them in many ways—only their use by cavalry units made the change of title necessary.

The first Combat Cars were developed in the early 1930s and a series of vehicles led to the standardisation of the Combat Car M1 by 1937. This was followed by the Combat Car M2 which had a trailing idler. These two light tanks formed the basis of all subsequent American light tank design until 1944. Their armament consisted of two .30-inch machine-guns and one .5-inch machine-gun. Their suspension was of the vertical volute type to be later adopted for nearly all American tanks. Very simply, this comprised two vertical springs attached to two road wheels. The operation was simple as was maintenance—a whole unit could be quickly and easily removed for change or repair, and it was this factor which was one of the main reasons for the American rejection of the Christie torsion bar suspension. The Combat

Combat Tank M1.

American Tanks of World War 2

Above *Light Tank M2A1.* **Above right** *Light Tank M2A4 in action with US Marines on Guadalcanal.* **Below right** *Light Tank M3 with riveted hull and turret.*

Car hulls were made from flat plates and as a result the vehicles had a rather 'slab-sided' look but were relatively easy to produce.

During 1940 the term 'Combat Car' was abolished and thus the Combat Car M1 became the Light Tank M1A1 and the M2 became the Light Tank M1A2. None were used operationally after 1941 but the two types were used extensively for training.

Light Tank M2

Parallel with the development of the Combat Car series during the early 1930s was the work carried out with the Light Tank T2 under the auspices of the infantry. The earlier light tanks had used a Vickers suspension but when the vertical volute suspension was shown to be superior, it was fitted to a trial vehicle, the Light Tank T2E1, which was standardised in late 1935 to become the Light Tank M2A1. Only 19 of these were made. The M2A1 was armed with one .30 and one .5-inch machine-gun mounted in a single turret plus another .30-inch machine-gun in the front of the hull. The next variant, M2A2, had the turret guns in two separate turrets. The third variant, the M2A3, had two turrets again but there were also changes to the suspension, most noticeable of which

was the trailing idler to be featured on all the later light tanks; some changes were also made to the engine installation.

The main production variant was the Light Tank M2A4. Like all the earlier M2 series this was developed at the Rock Island Arsenal. The main change from the earlier versions was that the armament became a 37 mm gun mounted in a single turret. A co-axial .30-inch machine-gun was fitted and two more were mounted in small sponsons on the hull front; an AA mount on the hull roof was also available. More changes were made to the engine compartment and there was a slight increase in all-round armour. The main wartime role of the M2A4 was for training, but a small number did see some action in the Pacific during a few of the early campaigns. A number were also sent to the UK but they were used for training only.

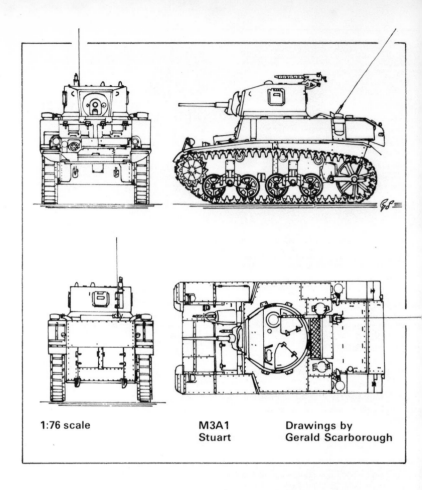

1:76 scale　　　　　**M3A1**　　　　**Drawings by**
　　　　　　　　　　　Stuart　　　　**Gerald Scarborough**

Data Light Tank M2A4

Weight in action	10,433 kg / 23,000 lb
Maximum road speed	40-48 kph / 25-30 mph
Maximum cross-country speed	29 kph / 18 mph
Road range	209 km / 130 miles
Length	4,420 mm / 174 inches
Height	2,489 mm / 98 inches
Width	2,470 mm / 97.25 inches
Engine horse power	250
Track width	193.7 mm / 7.625 inches
Wheel base	1,854 mm / 73 inches
Armament	1 × 37 mm
	3 × .30-inch machine-guns
Ammunition carried	103 × 37 mm
	7,185 × .30 inch
Front armour	25 mm / 0.98 inch
Crew	4

Light Tank M3

The lessons observed during the European campaigns of 1940 led to a gradual development of the light tank series into the Light Tank M3. In this version there were several improvements, including thicker armour and a strengthened suspension to carry the extra weight. The trailing idler wheel was increased in size and lowered to improve stability when on the move. Numerically, the M3 was the most important of the light tanks as 5,811 were made and the type was used all over the world by the US Army. It was freely issued to Allied armies, of which one of the more important was the British, where the M3 was known as the Stuart.

As the production run of the M3 continued, many improvements were fed into the line. One of the first changes was to the turret where riveted construction gave way to a new welded design. This, in turn was replaced by a cast/welded turret, and during 1942 the riveted hull was replaced by a welded hull. Combat experience in North Africa with the British led to the introduction of two extra jettisonnable fuel tanks. To complicate matters, 500 M3s were fitted with Guiberson diesel engines in place of the Continental 7-cylinder petrol engine. In British service these were known as the Stuart II (the standard M3 was the Stuart I). With all these detail changes being gradually introduced it will be appreciated that the early M3 configuration was very different from the later versions. The last M3s went out of production in August 1942. In service they were found to be fast and reliable and well suited to the reconnaissance role, and they remained in service until 1945 with many armies.

Other versions were as follows: —

M3A1 Followed the M3 on the production lines. This version had the turret cupola removed and the hull machine-guns taken from the side sponsons — in service these were found to be of limited value and their removal increased the internal stowage space. The first versions had a riveted hull but this was gradually replaced by a welded

Top *Light Tank M3 with welded turret and riveted hull.* **Above** *Light Tank M3A1.*

hull. A basket was fitted to the turret, and again, some tanks were fitted with the Guiberson engine. In British use, the M3A1 became the Stuart III and the Guiberson-engined version became the Stuart IV.

M3A2 This designation was not used. It was to have been applied to the welded hull version of the M3A1 but in the end no differentiation was made between them.

M3A3 This was the final production version and featured a redesigned all-welded hull which, as well as providing a better shape for shot deflection, gave more space inside. This increase in internal space was used to provide more fuel capacity and ammunition stowage. Sandshields were fitted as standard. The M3A3 entered production in early 1943. In British service the M3A3 was known as the Stuart V.

M3 Command Tank M3s in all versions were often modified by removing their turrets and replacing them with a welded steel box. This box was usually open and a .5-inch machine-gun was fitted as armament.

In this form the M3 was used as a command tank, and extra radios were usually installed.

The M3 series was used for a number of trials, often with engine installations and transmissions. Other items of equipment tested were mine exploders, flamethrowers and flame guns, duplex drive components and AA turrets. Other trial vehicles were used to test the fitting of 75 mm and 3-inch guns but none of these passed the trial stages.

Data M3A1

Weight in action	12,927 kg/28,500 lb
Maximum road speed	60 kph/36 mph
Maximum cross-country speed	32 kph/20 mph
Road range	112.6 km/70 miles
Length	4,540 mm/178.75 inches
Width	2,235 mm/88 inches
Height	2,299 mm/90.5 inches
Engine horse power	250 or 220 (Guiberson)
Track width	295 mm/11.625 inches
Wheel base	1,854 mm/73 inches
Armament	1 × 37 mm
	4 × .30-inch machine-guns
Ammunition carried	116 × 37 mm
	8,270 × .30-inch
Front armour	38 mm/1.5 inches
Side armour	25.4 mm/1 inch
Turrent front armour	38 mm/1.5 inches
Crew	4

Light Tank M5

By late 1941 production of the M3 series was well under way, but with the rapid expansion in demand for tanks of all kinds there came a shortage of nearly all forms of components, not the least of which were engines and especially the Continental engines used in the M3. During late 1941 the motor firm of Cadillac suggested that two of their engines could be used to power the light tanks and a trial vehicle, the M3E2, was fitted with Cadillac engines and an automatic transmission. The conversion proved a success as the engines were smooth-running and the automatic transmission made the vehicle easy to drive. The conversion was ordered into production by Cadillac (who had to clear their car production line) as the Light Tank M4 but this was later changed to Light

Tank M5 to prevent confusion with the Medium Tank M4.

To accommodate the large coupled engines, the rear deck was raised. The

American Tanks of World War 2

rest of the vehicle was similar to the M3A1 and featured a welded hull. A later version was the M5A1 which raised the modification level to bring it into line with the improvements made on the M3A3. These improvements included a turret bulge to accommodate a radio, an improved mount for the turret gun and larger crew hatches. The M5A1 followed the M5 on the production lines in early 1943 by which time extra production lines had been set up away from the Cadillac plant.

In service, the M5 and M5A1 proved even more popular than the M3 series.

They were easy to drive, had a smoother ride, and were reliable. They were used all over the world and were issued to many Allied armies. Britain received a number which were known as the Stuart VI.

There were a number of variants based on the M5 which are listed below. A number were also used for various engine and transmission trials. Some were used to test amphibious warfare components.

M5 Command Tank As M3 Command Tank.

Above *Light Tank M3A3.*

Left *Light Tank M5 with Cullin hedgerow device.*

Right *Light Tanks M5A1 in action in Germany.*

American tank data

M5 with flame warfare equipment
The service version of flamethrower used on the M5 was the E7-7 flame gun (this could also be fitted to the M3A1). Trials were carried out with the E8 and E9-9 flame guns but they did not pass the prototype stage.

M5 Dozer This was an M5 with the turret removed and a bulldozer blade fitted—some retained the turret. This conversion was made in 1944.

Mortar Motor Carriages There were three of these. The T27 and T27E1, both based on the M5A1, were open vehicles fitted with the 81 mm mortar; the T29 was fitted with a 4.2-inch mortar. None of these conversions proved satisfactory and none passed the trials stage.

T8 Reconnaissance Vehicle This was a 'Limited standard' vehicle consisting of a turretless M5 fitted with a .5-inch machine-gun in a ring mounting. Numbers of old M5s were converted and used in action during 1944 and 1945. The T8E1 was a version fitted with land-mine racks.

M5A1 with Psy-war Equipment This was a standard M5A1 fitted with loudspeakers used to spread propoganda in the front lines. Used 1944-1945.

Howitzer Motor Carriage M8 By 1942 requests had been made to fit a 75 mm howitzer to the light tank series. After a series of trials a version of the M5, the T47, was fitted with an enlarged turret mounting a 75 mm howitzer. This became the Howitzer Motor Carriage M8 and from September 1942 until January 1944 Cadillac turned out a total of 1,778. The M8 was used extensively in North-West Europe and Italy as part of the medium tank battalions. The M5 hull was altered by the fitting of an escape hatch for the driver in the hull front but few other changes were necessary.

T82 Howitzer Motor Carriage This was a trial vehicle with a 75 mm howitzer mounted in a limited-traverse mount on the hull front. It was intended for jungle warfare but it was abandoned in May 1945.

Data M5A1

Weight in action	15,380 kg / 33,907 lb
Maximum road speed	60 kph / 36 mph
Maximum cross-country speed	38.6 kph / 24 mph
Road range	161 km / 100 miles
Length	4,839 mm / 190.5 inches
Width	2,241.5 mm / 88.25 inches
Height	2,299 mm / 90.5 inches
Engine horse power	220
Track width	295 mm / 11.625 inches
Wheel base	1,867 mm / 73.5 inches
Armament	1 × 37 mm
	2 or 3 × .30-inch machine-guns
Ammunition carried	147 × 37 mm
	6,500 × .30-inch
Front armour	54 mm / 2.125 inches
Side armour	25.4 mm / 1 inch
Turret front armour	44.5 mm / 1.75 inches
Crew	4

Light Tank T7

In January 1941 calls were already being made for a new light tank to replace the existing models. The new tank was intended to be more powerful and better armoured than the existing vehicles and the Rock Island Arsenal designed and produced a prototype, the T7. This design had a 37 mm gun

Medium Tank M7.

but a later version, the T7E2 had a 57 mm gun, a cast turret and a welded hull. This version was produced in June 1942 but then it was decided to fit a 75 mm gun and this took the vehicle out of the light tank category into the medium tank range and the design then became the Medium Tank M7.

While the various prototypes were being produced a new tank arsenal was being built at Bettendorf, Iowa. There, mass production of over 3,000 M7s was planned but by the time a 75 mm gun had been installed into the M7 the suspension was overloaded and the vehicle was seriously underpowered. Also, by that time the Medium Tank M4 was in full-scale production and service and another medium tank would only have led to difficulties. Thus the M7 was dropped, and the Bettendorf Arsenal turned to other things after only seven M7s had been produced. The whole project was an expensive failure, and one of the few examples of American war planning going badly wrong.

Light Tank (Airborne) M22

By early 1941 a need had been foreseen for a light tank capable of being transported by air for use during an airborne campaign. The result was a design by Marmon-Herrington that was produced in prototype form by late 1941 as the T9. This small tank mounted a 37 mm gun and as it had to be light, armour was thin. Changes were made to the hull shape and such items as power traverse for the turret, and the gun gyro-stabiliser, were removed to save weight still further. This resulted in the T9E1 which was standardised as the Light Tank (Airborne) M22 in early 1943.

Production ended in February 1944 but the M22 was destined never to go into action with the American forces as they lacked a suitable transport for it. The only aircraft they had that could carry the M22 was the C-54 Skymaster but even then the tank had to be ferried slung under the fuselage with the turret removed and carried inside the aircraft. This was hardly a viable tactical proposition. As a result large numbers of M22s were issued under Lease-Lend to the British airborne units who had a glider large enough to carry the M22, the Hamilcar, and small numbers were used by the British during the Rhine crossings of March 1945. In British service the M22 was known as the Locust.

In action the M22 would have been of very limited value. Its light armament and thin armour would have placed it at a distinct tactical disadvantage if it had ever confronted even the lightest enemy tanks after 1943.

American tank data

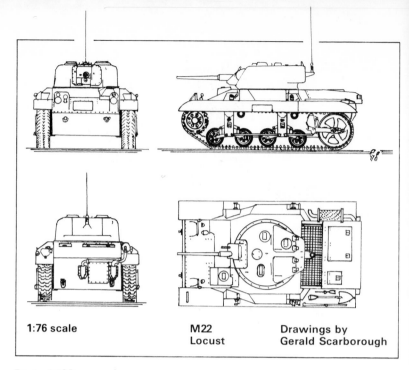

1:76 scale   M22   Drawings by
                           Locust   Gerald Scarborough

Data M22

Weight in action	7,445 kg / 16,400 lb
Maximum road speed	64 kph / 40 mph
Maximum cross-country speed	48 kph / 30 mph
Road range	217 km / 135 miles
Length	3,937 mm / 155 inches
Width	2,159 mm / 85 inches
Height	1,854 mm / 73 inches
Engine horse power	162
Track width	286 mm / 11.25 inches
Wheel base	1,791 mm / 70.5 inches
Armament	1 × 37 mm
	1 × .30-inch machine-gun
Ammunition carried	50 × 37 mm
	2,500 × .30 inch
Front armour	25 mm / 0.98 inch
Crew	3

Light Tank M24

By 1942 it was becoming obvious that the days of the 37 mm gun as a tank weapon were nearing an end and a call was made for a light tank with a more powerful gun, preferably a 75 mm weapon. Attempts to fit a 75 mm gun in M5 experimental vehicles proved unsuccessful. A new design was the answer and during late 1943 a new vehicle, the Light Tank T24, was produced. The new tank had many features of the old M5 such as the twin Cadillac engines and automatic transmission, and indeed the T24 was a

28   American Tanks of World War 2

Light (Airborne) tank M22 embarking on a C-82.

Cadillac venture. The 75 mm gun was a remarkable piece of design work as it was originally the well-known French '75'. This gun, dating from the Great War, had been developed into an aircraft gun during the late 1930s and early 1940s and as a result it was considerably lightened and reduced in size. By 1943 the use of heavy aircraft guns was falling into a state of neglect as the aircraft rocket took over, but the gun was just the thing for the confines of a light tank turret.

The T24 was standardised in May 1944 by which time it was already in its initial production stages. The T24 became the Light Tank M24 and was later given the extra name Chaffee. The M24 went into full-scale production with orders for up to 5,000 vehicles and the first Chaffees entered service in late 1944. Some were shipped to Europe where they arrived to take a small part in the fighting that led to the end of the war in Europe. After the war

the M24 went on to become one of the more important American tanks and it played a major role during the campaign in Korea.

One of the more important features of the M24 was that its chassis was selected as the basis for a whole range of special purpose vehicles. This was part of an American policy to produce a 'combat team' of vehicles all sharing a common chassis which would greatly simplify maintenance and logistic problems which the range of different vehicles in service by 1944 was causing. The M24 was the basis of the 'Light Weight Combat Team', and other vehicles in the medium and heavy categories will be mentioned later in the book. The range of vehicles based on the M24 are described below.

M19 Gun Motor Carriage Developed from the T65, this vehicle carried two 40 mm Bofors AA guns. By May 1945 only 285 had been produced and the type went on to a long post-war career.

M37 Howitzer Motor Carriage This carried a 105 mm howitzer. Developed from the T76 this was not standardised

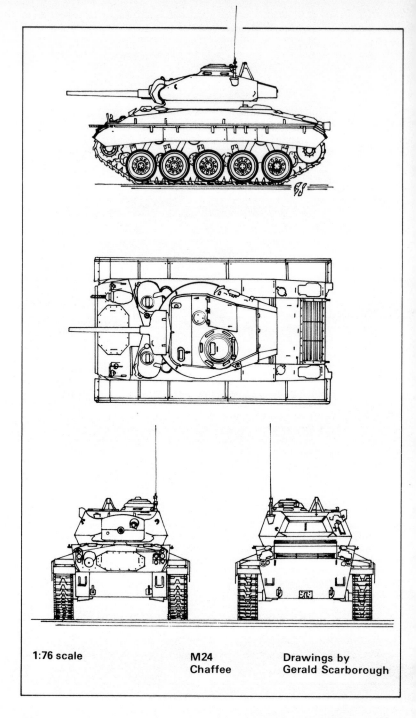

1:76 scale

M24
Chaffee

Drawings by
Gerald Scarborough

American Tanks of World War 2

M24 Light Tanks of the US Ninth Army board assault craft for the crossing of the Upper Rhine.

until November 1944 and most of the production was carried out after the war ended.

M41 Howitzer Motor Carriage This vehicle was developed from the T64E1 and carried a 155 mm howitzer situated at the rear of the chassis. Standardisation did not take place until May 1945 and most of the production total was built after the war ended. Unofficially known as 'Gorilla'.

T38 Mortar Motor Carriage 4.2-inch mortar in a modified M37. Project cancelled.

T77E1 Multiple Gun Motor Carriage Quad .5-inch machine-guns in a special turret. Project cancelled.

As was usual with American tanks, the M24 was used for a whole series of development trials and experiments with engines, guns, etc, and many of them were carried out post-war.

Data M24

Weight in action	18,370 kg/40,500 lb
Maximum road speed	56 kph/35 mph
Maximum cross-country speed	40 kph/25 mph
Road range	161 km/100 miles
Length less gun	4,991 mm/196.5 inches
Length with gun	5,486 mm/216 inches
Width	2,946 mm/116 inches
Height	2,476.5 mm/97.5 inches
Engine horse power	220
Track width	406 mm/16 inches
Wheel base	2,438 mm/96 inches
Armament	1 × 75 mm M6
	2 × .30-inch machine-guns
	1 × .5-inch machine-gun
Ammunition carried	48 × 75 mm
	4,125 × .30-inch
	420 × .5-inch
Front armour	25.4 mm/1 inch
Side and rear armour	19 mm/0.75 inch
Turret front armour	38 mm/1.5 inches
Crew	5

American tank data

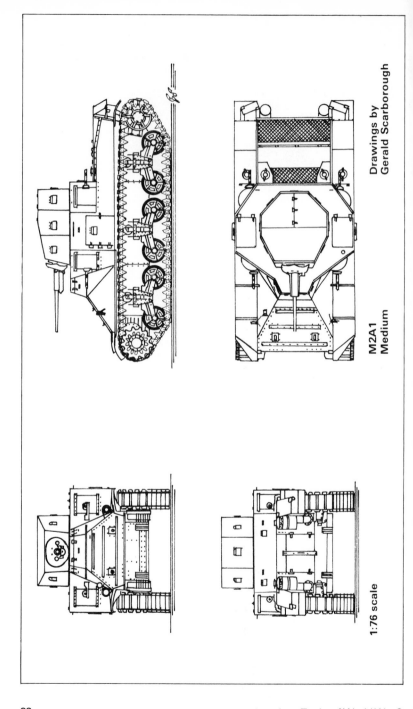

Drawings by
Gerald Scarborough

M2A1
Medium

1:76 scale

American Tanks of World War 2

Light Tank T16

The Light Tank T16 was a two-man tank built by Marmon-Herrington to a Lend-Lease order for China and the Dutch East Indies. In the event these were not delivered and as production ran to 240 vehicles the total were taken over by the US War Department and issued to the US Army for training purposes. Some were used as 'policing' and garrison tanks in Alaska and the Aleutians. They received the designation Light Tank T16 and were a limited procurement issue. Armament was a single .30-inch machine-gun with another for use on an AA pintle.

The Medium Tanks

Up until the late 1930s development of any tank that would exceed the 15-ton bridging limit imposed by Congress quite simply did not take place, but by 1938 work had begun on a new medium tank design, the T5. This design underwent a protracted development period and was eventually standardised in June 1939 as the Medium Tank M2. The M2 design was virtually an enlarged Light Tank M2 and

T5E2 test vehicle with 75mm Pack Howitzer mounted in hull front.

featured many identical components, including the Continental engine. The gun was the same 37 mm weapon as fitted to the light tank and the suspension units were the same vertical volute items, but the number each side was increased to three. But the Medium Tank M2 did reflect the concept of the tank being used in the infantry support role as it was almost covered in machine-guns. Two were fixed in the hull front, and further four were emplaced in traversable sponsons around the hull — the rear two could be fired at fixed deflection plates on the hull rear to deflect the fire downwards as the tank crossed trenches. A further two machine-guns were fixed to the turret sides. Overall the layout suggested the shape of the later medium tanks.

Production of a batch of 15 vehicles began in August 1939, but soon afterwards a revised version, the M2A1, was produced. This had thicker armour and a larger turret, and the engine was uprated from 350 to 400 bhp. The M2A1 was selected for mass production and a new arsenal, the Detroit Tank Arsenal, was built to produce the huge numbers needed to equip the expanding Allied armies. But the events of May 1940 when the Germans flooded across the Low Countries and France drove home the point that a medium tank armed with

only a 37 mm gun was obsolete. Thus the M2A1 did not enter large scale production and only 94 were made, most of which ended up being used for training and a number of trials.

Perhaps the most important trial vehicle in the series was the Medium Tank T5E2. This was a much modified T5 (actually the M2 prototype) with a 75 mm howitzer mounted in the hull front. Although the configuration was a trial only, it did point to the feasibility of a hull-mounted 75 mm weapon, which in turn led to the 75 mm gun arrangement adopted on the Medium Tank M3.

Data Medium Tank M2A1

Weight in action	21,337 kg / 47,040 lb
Maximum road speed	42 kph / 26 mph
Maximum cross-country speed	27.6 kph / 17.2 mph
Road range	209 km / 130 miles
Length	5,334 mm / 210 inches
Width	2,591 mm / 102 inches
Height	2,819 mm / 111 inches
Engine horse power	400
Track width	357 mm / 14 inches
Wheel base	2,057 mm / 81 inches
Armament	1 × 37 mm
	8 × .30-inch machine-guns
Ammunition carried	200 × 37 mm
	12,250 × .30-inch
Front armour	32 mm / 1.26 inches
Crew	6

Medium Tank M3

Although the need or a medium tank with a 75 mm gun was driven home during the 1940 campaigns in Europe, the American neglect of the medium tank meant that producing such a vehicle was not an easy task. The only medium tank on hand was the M2 which was unsuitable for battle. However, it could be adapted to take a 75 mm gun in a side sponson while a new design with a 75 mm turret gun was developed. Feasibility studies with the T5E2 had shown that a side-mounted gun was a viable proposition

Medium Tank M2A1.

American Tanks of World War 2

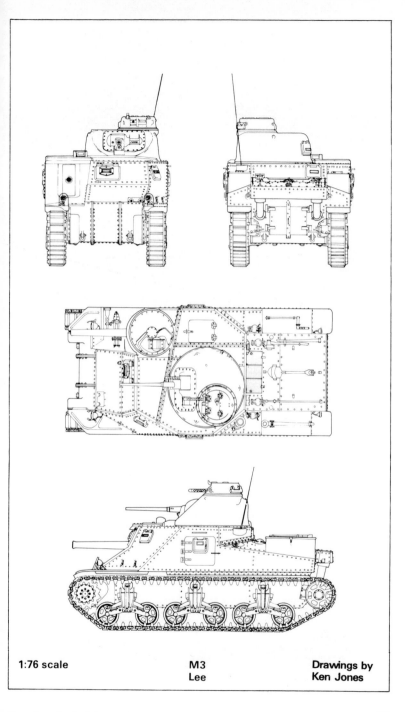

1:76 scale   **M3**   **Drawings by**
                            Lee   **Ken Jones**

American tank data   35

although the gun traverse would be considerably restricted. But the main problem then was to produce a 75 mm gun as no suitable weapon was available. Once again the French '75' was taken as a starting point and modified into a tank gun. There were two versions of this gun, the M2 and the M3, the main difference being that the latter was longer. This had an unfortunate effect as the shorter M2 was the first version produced. When installed in the side mounting of the Medium Tank M3 the difference in length had an effect on the gyro-stabiliser which was being used in a tank for the first time. The stabilisers were preset to accommodate the longer M3 gun and the gear could only work with the short M2 gun if a counterweight was placed round the muzzle. In time the M2 guns were replaced by the M3.

But the aside mention of the 75 mm gun pre-empts the development of the Medium Tank M3. Very basically, the M2 design was adapted to take the new 75 mm gun in a side sponson and a turret mounting a 37 mm gun was situated on top of the hull. The multiple machine-guns of the M2 were eliminated. The external dimensions were little altered, as was the suspension. The Medium Tank M3 was ordered straight 'off the drawing board' with no trial vehicles being produced.

Initial production of the M3 was very difficult as the main tank arsenal, then still under construction near Detroit, was meant for M2A1 production and much of the tooling and jigs had to be altered or changed to suit the new vehicle. Engines were another problem as demand for the Continental engines soon outstripped supply and a variety of other engines had to be fitted resulting in a number of variants (see list below). Plants other than the

Right *American armour on manoeuvres in England with early production M3 tanks armed with the M2 gun.*

Left *M3 Medium Tanks armed with M3 75mm guns on manoeuvres in England.*

American Tanks of World War 2

Far left *Medium Tank M3, pilot model.*

Left *Late production M3 with side doors eliminated.*

Right *Medium Tank M3A1 with cast hull armed with M2 75mm gun.*

Detroit Arsenal also started to produce the M3. Design work on the vehicle was finished in March 1941 and the first models rolled off the lines the following month, a most remarkable example of the latent power of American industry.

The construction methods used for the M3 were a mixture of the conventional and the modern. Much of the hull was constructed from flat plates riveted together, but the 37 mm gun turret and the sponson were both cast items. As production continued many changes were introduced, the most noticeable of which was the fitting of an all-cast hull. To simplify and create a stronger structure the side doors fitted to early production versions were eliminated. There were numerous other modifications as well, but one that actually changed the turret shape was due to the actions of the British Tank Mission.

This Mission visited the USA in June 1940 in an attempt to procure tanks to replace their huge losses in the events leading up to Dunkirk. They ordered large numbers of M3s but as they were paying cash for them they insisted on a few changes. One was to the turret which had to be lower and feature a rear bulge to accommodate a radio. Other internal changes were made to suit British equipment. The British called their version of the M3 the Grant and the first examples to see action went into battle at Gazala in North Africa in May 1942. There the 75 mm gun at last gave the British tank crews some sort of parity with the German who were by then mounting long 75 mm guns on their tanks. After March 1941 the introduction of the Lease-Lend Act enabled the British to receive numbers of the unmodified M3, which they called the Lee.

Production of the M3 ended in

Above *Medium Tank M3A2 with welded hull.* **Below** *Medium Tank M3A5.*

December by which time 6,258 had been made. Many M3s were issued to Allied armies, including the Russian. For all its success as a fighting tank, the M3 was limited on many occasions by the restricted traverse of the hull gun and as a result they were replaced by later tanks as soon as possible. The M3 then took on a new lease of life as its roomy hull enabled it to be modified into a whole host of special purpose vehicles, (for a list of the 'British' conversions, see *Airfix Magazine Guide No 17*). Most of these conversions are listed below, but it must be added that many old M3s were shipped to the Far East where they were in action right until the end of the war in 1945.

M3 Basic production model. Fitted with Continental 340 hp engine. 4,924 were made, more than any other single version. British Lee I.

M3A1 Cast hull in place of normal riveted construction. British Lee II.

M3A2 Small run of 12 with welded hull.

M3A3 M3A2 with twin General Electric diesels giving 375 hp. British Lee IV.

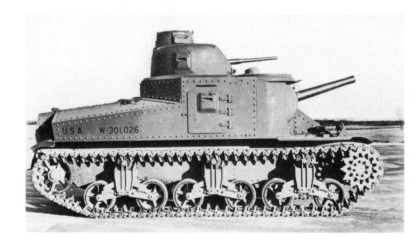

American Tanks of World War 2

Above *Medium Tank M3A4, hull lengthened to accommodate longer engine.*

M3A4 M3 fitted with Chrysler Multibank engine giving 370 hp. The introduction of this bulky engine made up from five commercial automobile engines meant a longer hull, track and suspension. British Lee VI.

M3A5 M3A3 with riveted hull.

Guiberson diesel engines were fitted to some M3 and M3A1 models.

M3 variants

Flame guns on M3s The E5E2-M3 flame gun was fitted to some M3s. It was issued as a kit and replaced the turret machine-gun. Trials were carried out with the E3 flame gun but were not continued into a service version.

M3 with Mine Exploder T1 This was a hang-over from the M2A1 which consisted of two roller units pushed in front of the tank and one single roller pulled behind. It was not a great success in use.

Tank Recovery Vehicle M31 Originally the T2, this was a conversion of an M3 with both guns replaced by dummies. A winch and boom were added at the rear and extra tools were carried. The M31B1 used the M3A3 chassis and the M3B2 used the M3A5.

Full-Track Prime Mover M33 Numbers of M31s were further converted to become 155 mm gun towers during 1943 and 1944. The turret and

boom were removed and a .5-inch machine-gun fitted where the turret had been. Extra equipment to suit the towing role was fitted.

3-inch Gun Motor Carriage T24 This was an attempt to place a 3-inch gun on to an M3 with the turret and sponson removed. The idea was to produce a form of tank destroyer but the end result was too high and complex and the project was cancelled.

3-inch Gun Motor Carriage T40 This was an attempt to use old 3-inch AA gun barrels in a modified form of M3 resembling the T24 mentioned above. Although the project was standardised as the M9 it was not proceeded with.

40 mm Gun Motor Carriage T36 Attempt to mount a 40 mm Bofors AA gun in an M3. The gun was mounted in a complex cast turret. Project cancelled

Shop Tractor T10 M3 fitted with British CDL turret. Not used in action despite production run of 355.

Heavy Tractor T16 1942 attempt to produce a heavy gun tractor. Not a success but the idea led to the Tank Recovery Vehicle M31.

Gun Motor Carriage M12 First tested in February 1942, this involved the fitting of a 155 mm gun to a much-modified M3 chassis. The engine was removed to the front of the hull and the gun was mounted at the rear. Only 100

were made and the last was produced during March 1943. At first they were used for training only but after June 1944 they were moved to Europe where they proved to be very useful weapons. **Cargo Carrier M30** Identical to the M12 but without the gun. These vehicles were used as ammunition and support vehicles for the latter.

In addition to the above M3s were used for many trial and experimental purposes.

Data Medium Tank M3

Weight in action	27,240 kg/60,000 lb
Maximum road speed	42 kph/26 mph
Maximum cross-country speed	25 kph/16 mph
Road range	193 km/120 miles
Length	5,639 mm/222 inches
Width	2,718 mm/107 inches
Height	3,124 mm/123 inches
Engine horse power	340
Track width	419 mm/16.5 inches
Wheel base	2,108 mm/83 inches
Armament	1 × 75 mm
	1 × 37 mm
	3 or 4 .30-inch machine-guns
Ammunition carried	46 × 75 mm
	178 × 37 mm
	9,200 × .30-inch
Front armour	51 mm/2 inches
Side and rear armour	38 mm/1.5 inches
Turret front armour	57 mm/2.25 inches
Crew	6

Although it has not been mentioned above, there was one further off-shoot from the Medium Tank M3 that was so important that it deserves a special mention. This was the Howitzer Motor Carriage M7. This was an M3 chassis with an open body mounting a 105 mm howitzer at the front. The first model was the T32 standardised in February 1942 to produce the M7. By late 1942, 2,028 had been produced. Large numbers were issued to the British who nicknamed the M7 the 'Priest', mainly due to the large 'pulpit' .5-inch

American Tanks of World War 2

Left *Tank Recovery Vehicle M31 lifting an M4A1 (76mm) tank.*

Right *Gun Motor Carriage M12 in action in Germany.*

Below *Howitzer Motor Carriage M7 in action in Italy.*

machine-gun mounting on the right of the vehicle. The introduction of the M7 into service greatly increased the ability of artillery units attached to mobile formations to keep up with the tanks, but for the British the introduction of a new artillery calibre was a complication, despite the compatability of many parts with the M3 and M4 series of medium tanks. With the US Army the M7 remained in use until 1945.

Medium Tank M4

As soon as the design work for the interim Medium Tank M3 had been completed in March 1941, the Ordnance Board designers turned their attentions to its successor. The new tank was to mount a 75 mm gun in a fully traversing turret, and it was this which caused many headaches when the final design form was chosen. The new turret was to be cast, but casting such a large component in armour plate was something that even American industry had not tried. However, the problems were overcome and the first model, the Medium Tank T6, was rolled out in September 1941.

The T6 was built on to the chassis of the earlier M3 and used the same suspension and engine. The hull was cast which not only made production quicker but gave increased shot deflection. The turret mounted the M2 75 mm gun as the intended M3 was still not available, but as on the M3 tank the gun

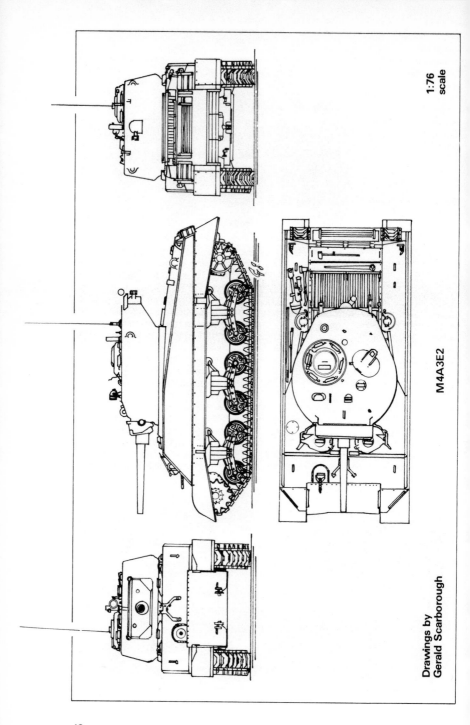

1:76
scale

M4A3E2

Drawings by
Gerald Scarborough

American Tanks of World War 2

Above *Medium Tank M4, early production.* **Above right** *Medium Tank M4, late production.*

was gyro-stabilised. The turret also housed the radio in a rear overhang. A throwback to the days of the Medium Tank M2 was the fitting of two fixed machine-guns in the hull front but this was not done on production models. Another feature designed out on production models was the side escape doors—this not only made production easier but also provided a stronger hull. Extra hatches were provided in the hull belly and above the front hull. In October 1941 the T6 was standardised as the Medium Tank M4 and production was scheduled to follow the M3 on the lines as soon as it could be arranged. But to facilitate production in some of the less technologically

advanced plants, a redesigned hull consisting of welded armour plates was designed. The version with welded plates became the M4 while the version with the cast hull became the M4A1.

The production plans for the M4 expanded rapidly to meet the target of 1,000 tanks a month (later to be doubled). At one point in 1942 no fewer than 11 separate plants were turning out the M4 and a special tank arsenal was built to produce it at Grand Blanc, Michigan. But no sooner was production under way than the perennial engine troubles cropped up again. The main problem yet again was the Wright Continental engine. This was really an aircraft engine and as the M4 pro-

Below *Medium Tanks M4A1 passing through a village in France.* **Below right** *Late production M4A1 Medium Tank operating in the Anzio beachhead area. Note the early M34 gun mount.*

American tank data

Left *Medium Tank M4A2, early production. Note the twin fixed machine-guns.*

Right *A Medium Tank M4A3 advances through a Belgian town.*

gramme got into its stride, so did a massive aircraft construction programme, so calls on the Continental reached the stage where alternative engines had to be fitted to the M4s coming off the lines. This raised the usual crop of variants.

By the time the various M4s were coming out, Lease-Lend was well under way and the British were among the first to receive substantial numbers. The first M4s to see action were a handful used at El Alamein in October 1942. Battle experience with these and others led to a constant stream of modifications being introduced on to the production lines and thus a host of

variants. These are listed below but it must be stressed that the tally is far from complete. By the time production ended in 1946 well over 40,000 M4 tanks had been produced (this total includes all the M4 variants and special purpose vehicles) and with such a huge total made it was inevitable that there would be a large number of hybrid variants, trial and experimental.

Main M4 variants

M4 Version with Continental engine and welded hull. British Sherman I.
M4A1 First version to go into produc-

American Tanks of World War 2

tion. As M4 but with cast hull. British Sherman II.

M4A2 Fitted with twin General Motors diesel engines. This version was not used by the Americans alone—very other armies under Lease-Lend. Some were used by the US Marine Corps. British Sherman III.

M4A3 The Ford engine fitted to this version was specially developed for tank use in the M4A3. This version was the vehicle most favoured for US Army use and almost the entire output was used by the Americans alone—very few went overseas for Lease-Lend. The M4A3 was selected as the basis for the 'Medium Weight Combat Team'. Only

Left *Late production M4A2 of the US Marines passing a Japanese blockhouse during the fighting on Peleliu Island.*

Right *Medium Tank M4A3.*

Above right *Medium tank M4A3 (76mm).*

American tank data

Above *Medium Tank M4 (105mm Howitzer).*

Left *Medium Tank M4A1 with 76mm gun M1A2 and horiztonal volute spring suspension.*

Below *Ready for the invasion, M4A1 and M4A4 Medium Tanks at an Ordnance Depot in England. Note the appliqué armour on the M4A4 tanks.*

American Tanks of World War 2

Above *Medium Tank M4A3 with 76mm gun M1A1 and HVSS suspension.*

Below right *Medium Tank M4A3 with 76mm gun M1A2 and HVSS suspension. Note sandbags for extra protection.*

Bottom right *Close-up of the appliqué armour welded on the turret.*

a few were used by the British as the Sherman IV.

M4A4 This version used the Chrysler Multibank engine and its bulk necessitated a slightly lengthened hull. British Sherman V.

M4A5 Designation not used as it was issued for the Canadian Ram tank.

M4A6 Only 75 examples of this version were made. It was fitted with a Caterpillar radial diesel engine in a lengthened hull.

All the above are mentioned in their initial form only. Perhaps the most important change later made was the fitting of a 76 mm gun to the M4A1, M4A2 and M4A3. This larger gun required the use of a larger turret which was taken direct from the experimental Medium Tank T23. The 76 mm gun was put into production in February 1944 and later versions were fitted with muzzle brakes.

The 105 mm howitzer was fitted in place of the 75 mm gun on the M4 and M4A3 after trials with the M4A4E1 and M4E5. Tanks fitted with the howitzer were used in the close support role

American tank data

Left *Medium Tank M4A4, late production.*

Below left *Assault Tank M4A3E2.*

Bottom *Medium Tank M4 with Rocket Launchers T34 await orders on a hillside near the Siegfried Line.*

with Medium Tank battalions. Put into production during early 1944.

The HVSS suspension was placed in production in the middle of 1944 and was used in conjunction with a new wide track. The new suspension used four wheels per unit in place of the previous two. Track covers were used with the new wider track.

One special tank version that rates a special mention is the Assault Tank M4A3E2. This was a special heavily armoured version produced to be used in the anticipated assault on the Siegfried Line in North-West Europe during 1944, but most of them were used for close infantry support instead. The extra weight reduced speed and the usual armament was the 75 mm gun although some were retrofitted with the 76 mm weapon. Armour thickness

American Tanks of World War 2

Above *M4A1 equipped with Dozer Blade M1.* **Below** *Rocket Launcher T34.*

was as much as 150 mm /5.9 inches on the turret front and up to 100 mm/ 3.9 inches on the hull.

Special equipment carried by the M4 series

The Cullin Prong This was a simple hedgerow cutting device fitted to the front of many tanks employed in the fighting that took place in the Normandy 'bocage' country soon after the invasion of June 6 1944. The 'prongs' enabled tanks to cut their way through the dense hedgerows which were otherwise a considerable tank obstacle.

Rocket Launcher T34 To enable the M4 to saturate large areas with high explosive rockets, the 'Calliope' was devised. It consisted of 60 rocket tubes carried in a frame above the turret and elevated by the gun barrel. The rockets were 114 mm/4.5 inches in diameter. The T34E1 and T34E2 featured a rearrangement of the barrels to reduce the rocket dispersion.

Rocket Launcher M17 Originally the T40, this launcher fired 20 7.2-inch rockets, and was known as the 'Whiz-bang'. The whole frame could be jettisonned if necessary.

Dozer Blade M1 This was standardised in 1944 and it was used by all types of the M4 series. The M1A1 was the version used by M4s with HVSS suspension.

Mine Exploder M1 Nicknamed the 'Aunt Jemima', this consisted of two large rollers pushed in front of an M4. Originally the T1E3, this anti-mine device was used for a while after the Normandy landings.

Mine Exploder T2 and T4 American designations for British Crab equipment used in small numbers by American forces in Europe.

Flame-throwers used on M4s E4R2-5R1, E4R3-5R1: the latter later became the M3-4-3. All were issued as kits to replace hull machine-gun; E4R4R 5-6RC; this had a longer range than the above; E6-R1: another kit to replace

Left *M4 Mobile Assault Bridge.*

Right *M4A1 with M3-4-3 flame thrower.*

the hull machine-gun; E7-7: this had a short tube which replaced the main gun and fuel was carried inside the hull. above.

POA This was a Pacific theatre improvisation using an old 105 mm howitzer barrel. The POA-CWS 75-H1 used the 75 gun barrel of the M4 while the POA-CWS 75-H2 enabled the main armament to be used.

Ronson Flame Gun A few tanks used by the US Marines carried this Canadian device.

Crocodile Four M4s only used this British equipment in Europe in late 1944.

Special purpose versions of the M4

Tank Recovery Vehicle M32 This was a revision of the basic M4 to suit it for the armoured recovery role. The turret became fixed and the gun was replaced by a 81 mm smoke mortar. A winch and A-frame jib were also fitted. The M32B1 used a M4A1 chassis, the M32B2 used the M4A2, the M32B3 was based on the M4A3 and the M32B4 used the M4A4 chassis.

Full Track Prime Mover M34 This was a M32 with all the ARV gear removed and replaced by equipment suiting the vehicle to tow heavy guns.

M4 Mobile Assault Bridge One of the many field modifications carried out on the M4 series was the Mobile Assault Bridge used in Italy. It was a two-track bridge placed by a gantry fitted in place of the gun.

Howitzer Motor Carriage M7B1 While the early M7 vehicles used the M3 chassis, the M7B1 utilised that of the M4A3.

Howitzer Motor carriage M7B1 shelling German positions west of the Rhine, in Alsace.

American Tanks of World War 2

Gun Motor Carriage M10 Originally the T35, this was an attempt made during 1942 to place a heavy gun for the tank destroyer role on a M4A2 chassis. The gun selected was the 3-inch M6, and standardisation of this vehicle, with the gun in an open-topped special turret, was made in June 1942 as the M10. The M10A1 used the M4A3 chassis. Retrofitted modifications included weights secured to the turret rear to improve balance.

Full Track Prime Mover M35 A

90mm Gun Motor Carriage M36.

number of M10A1s had their turrets removed to convert them for towing heavy artillery.

Gun Motor Carriage M36 As a possible counter to the German use of heavy anti-tank guns, it was decided in late 1942 to mount the 90 mm AA gun in a tank. Attempts to fit the gun in an M10 were unsuccessful so a new turret was developed and the type was standardised as the M36 in June 1944. In action the M36 proved a very successful tank destroyer and saw action in Europe from late 1944 onwards. The M36B1 used a standard M4A3 chassis and hull while the M36B2 used the M10 chassis.

American tank data

Data Medium Tank M4A3

Weight in action	32,284 kg / 71,175 lb
Maximum road speed	47 kph / 29 mph
Maximum cross-country speed	32 kph / 20 mph
Road range	161 km / 100 miles
Length with gun	7,518 mm / 296 inches
Length less gun	6,274 mm / 247 inches
Width	2,680 mm / 105.5 inches
Height	3,426 mm / 134.875 inches
Engine horse power	450
Track width (vertical volute)	419 mm / 16.5 inches
Track width (HVSS)	584 mm / 23 inches
Wheel base	2,108 mm / 83 inches
Armament	1 × 76 mm
	2 × .30-inch machine-guns
	1 × .5-inch machine-gun
Ammunition carried	71 × 76 mm
	6,250 × .30-inch
	600 × .5-inch
Front armour	63.5 mm / 2.5 inches
Side and front armour	38 mm / 1.5 inches
Turret front armour	63.5 mm / 2.5 inches
Crew	5

The Heavy Tanks

As early as May 1940 the Ordnance Board were asked to design a heavy tank with a gun larger than the 75 mm weapon then being planned for the medium tanks. After a number of designs had been considered it was

Assault Tank T14.

decided to build the prototype of a tank with a single turret mounting a single 3-inch gun with a co-axial 37 mm gun. This became the Heavy Tank T1 and initial production plans for 100 were made in February 1941, this total later being increased to 250.

The number of prototypes was increased to four to test possible engine installations and drive systems. The T1E1 had a cast hull and electric trans-

American Tanks of World War 2

Heavy Tank M6.

mission while the T1E2 had a torque converter. The third vehicle, T1E3, had a welded hull and torque converter, while the fourth project, the T1E4, was cancelled as it was to have had an advanced twin diesel/torque converter system that would have taken too long to develop. In April 1942 the T1E2 was standardised as the Heavy Tank M6 after some protracted teething troubles, and later the T1E3 became the M6A1. Even later the T1E1 was standardised to become the M6A2.

Almost as soon as plans for production were made they were revised. By September 1942 the rapid armament expansion programme called for 5,000 M6s, but as this would have caused a disproportionate disruption of the tank programme it was cut back drastically to only 115 and even then, only 40 were ever made. The main reasons for this cut back were both political and military. The political reasons were caused by the fact that many politicians in the US Government had been hostile

to the heavy tank concept from the beginning and saw no need for such a vehicle. The military also found the M6 to be unsatisfactory in many ways — the internal layout was unsatisfactory, the engine and drives were still underdeveloped and caused many troubles, and overall the tank was thought to be too large and bulky. As a result the military concentrated on the development and production of the medium tank and the Heavy Tank M6 never did see action.

When the M6 first appeared it was the most powerful tank in the world and it would undoubtedly been able to prove itself a match for the later German Tiger and Panther, but it was a bulky machine and would have taken up a considerable amount of shipping space if there had ever been a demand for it in Europe or elsewhere. By the time it was ready the troops in the field were calling for medium tanks and the M6 took the shipping space of two mediums. Thus the M6 faded from the scene and those produced were used for a number of trials, many of which were related to the later heavy tanks.

American tank data

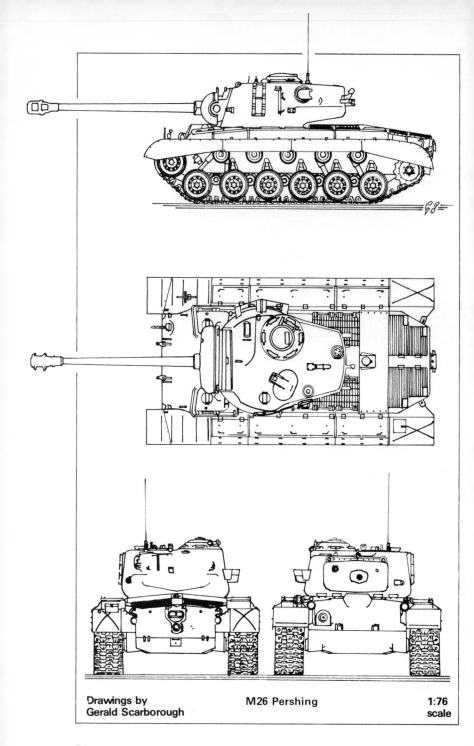

Drawings by
Gerald Scarborough

M26 Pershing

1:76
scale

American Tanks of World War 2

Data Heavy Tank M6

Weight in action	57,379 kg / 126,500 lb
Maximum road speed	35.4 kph / 22 mph
Road range	161 km / 100 miles
Length with gun	8,433 mm / 332 inches
Width	3,111.5 mm / 122.5 inches
Height	3,226 mm / 127 inches
Engine horse power	800
Track width	654 mm / 25.75 inches
Wheel base	2,362 mm / 93 inches
Armament	1 × 3-inch
	1 × 37 mm
	3 × .5-inch machine-guns
	2 × .30-inch machine-guns
Ammunition carried	75 × 3-inch
	202 × 37 mm
	5,700 × .5-inch
	7,500 × .30-inch
Front armour	76 mm / 3 inches
Side and rear armour	64 mm / 2.5 inches
Turret front armour	100 mm / 3.93 inches
Crew	6

Following on from the early contacts between the British Tank Commission and the US Ordnance Department, the Americans paid a great deal of attention to British combat experience and operational reports. During late 1941 the British expressed a need for a heavily armoured tank armed with a powerful gun for close support work. As a result the Americans came up with a design that incorporated features from both the Medium Tank M4 and the Heavy Tank M6. The result was the Assault Tank T14 and plans were made to produce up to 8,500 but the first pilot models were not produced until 1943. By then the British need for such a tank was already being met by the Churchill series and interest in the American T14 waned. The whole project was dropped in late 1944. The Assault Tank T14 had a 75 mm gun and armour was up to 133 mm/5.23 inches thick. It used a 520 hp petrol engine which gave maximum of speed of 35.4 kph/22 mph. Battle weight was

Heavy Tank M26 (General Pershing) passing through the town of Magdeburg.

American tank data

55

Heavy Tank T28/GMC T95. Note the double tracks.

38,102 kg/84,000 lb. Only two pilot models were produced.

Heavy Tank M26

Almost as soon as the Medium Tank M4 series was in production, a new design was under construction. This resulted in a long string of experimental vehicles which gradually increased in weight and striking power. The first of this line was the Medium Tank T20 which was developed into the T22. Then came the T23 which had a number of features that were tried on prototype vehicles and then introduced on to the Medium Tank M4 production lines. These features included such items as the T23 turret and 76 mm gun, the HVSS suspension and 47° hull front. With the T25 the HVSS and vertical volute suspension were abandoned in favour of a new torsion bar suspension, but almost as soon as the T25 was produced the T26, with thicker armour and a 90 mm gun, was pressed into favour by the appearance in battle of the German Tiger and Panther with heavy guns. Although these vehicles had been known to exist for some time it was not until 1944 that an effort to produce a heavy tank to counter them was made, and even then there were many who considered that the answer was the tank destroyer rather than the tank.

The result was that the T26 passed from the medium tank bracket and became the Heavy Tank T26E1 in June 1944. The tank/tank destroyer argument continued until late 1944 when the German Ardennes offensive at last tipped the scales in favour of the heavy tank. A developed model of the T26, the T26E3, was standardised as the Heavy Tank M26 and named the 'General Pershing'. That was in March 1945 so the M26 was too late to see action in Europe but numbers were used in the Pacific theatre before the war ended.

The Heavy Tank M26 was selected as the component for the 'Heavy Weight Combat Team' and a number of special purpose vehicles were developed using the M26 chassis. However, most of them were developed after the war ended and are thus outside the scope of this book. Most of the early changes such as the M26E1 and M26E4 were concerned with producing a more powerful 90 mm gun, but none saw service before the war ended. The T26E2, later the M45, mounted a 105 mm howitzer but only a few were produced.

American Tanks of World War 2

The Heavy Tank M26 was a very powerful tank and undoubtedly the most advanced of all the American tanks to see service. After 1945 it went on to a long period of development and in the shape of the Medium Tank M48 its successors are still in widespread use.

Data Heavy Tank M26

Weight in action	41,730 kg / 92,000 lb
Maximum road speed	48 kph / 30 mph
Maximum cross-country speed	8.4 kph / 5.2 mph
Road range	148 km / 92 miles
Length with gun	8,788 mm / 346 inches
Length of hull	6,452 mm / 254 inches
Height	2,769 mm / 109 inches
Width	3,505 mm / 138 inches
Engine horse power	500
Track width	609.6 mm / 24 inches
Wheel base	2,794 mm / 110 inches
Armament	1 × 90 mm
	1 × .5-inch machine-gun
	2 × .30-inch machine-guns
Ammunition carried	70 × 90 mm
	550 × .5-inch
	5,000 × .30-inch
Front armour	101.6 mm / 4 inches
Side armour	76 mm / 3 inches
Rear armour	50.8 mm / 2 inches
Turret front armour	101.6 mm / 4 inches
Crew	5

One further heavy tank remains to be mentioned, the Heavy Tank T28, later to be re-designated the Gun Motor Carriage T95. This was a super-heavy vehicle that was meant to be invulnerable to all known tanks and capable of mounting the newly-developed 105 mm gun. As the 105 mm gun was not mounted in a turret the vehicle was re-designated a Gun Motor Carriage in March 1945 when work on one of the two prototypes was under way, and the first example was not finished until September 1945, just after the war ended. The T28/T95 was a massive vehicle similar in many ways to the British 'Tortoise'. It was a low, heavily armoured vehicle with the unusual feature of two rows of tracks on each side. On the T28/T95 the outer row could be removed for ease of handling during transportation or could be joined together and then towed behind the vehicle when travelling on roads. Maximum armour thickness was 300 mm/11.8 inches, and weight in action would have been a hefty 86,260 kg/190,000 lb, ie 84.8 tons. Maximum speed was only 12.8 kph/8 mph.

The Tank Destroyer concept

One anomaly that grew up in the US armoured formations was the creation of a Tank Destroyer force. This grew out of the precept that the best weapon to use against the tank was the gun, but a gun that was placed in a light, fast vehicle to give it the maximum mobility. Thus there were developed a number of Tank Destroyer vehicles that looked like tanks but were in fact highly specialised vehicles with large calibre guns, thin armour and powerful engines. In order to place the guns on existing tank chassis the turrets were open. Their role in action was to literally

American tank data

Above *76mm GMC M18.* **Right** *3-inch GMC M10.*

destroy enemy tanks to enable armoured columns to gain the room needed for their mobile tactics.

The Tank Destroyer Arm grew to a maximum size of 106 battalions in early 1943, at which time their main armament was the Gun Motor Carriage M10 and M10A1. Later these were supplemented by the Gun Motor Carriage M36. Both these vehicles were based on the chassis of the Medium

90mm GMC M36.

Tank M4 and mounted 3-inch and 90 mm guns respectively. Both types dispensed with armour in favour of speed and striking power but they were essentially adaptations of existing vehicles. One vehicle that was developed specifically for the Tank Destroyer role was the Gun Motor Carriage M18.

The M18 had a long gestation period as it originally stemmed from a requirement for a tank destroyer with a 37 mm gun. This was gradually up-gunned until the Gun Motor Carriage T70 was armed with a 76 mm gun. This vehicle featured parts intended for use with the Light Tank M24 but had a shorter suspension and track. The T70 was standardised in February 1944 as the Gun Motor Carriage M18, and was unofficially known as the 'Hellcat'. Total number produced was 2,507 and production ceased in October 1944.

In action the Hellcat proved itself to be a most successful weapon. Its power-to-weight ratio made it the fastest American tracked vehicle to see

58

service and its 76 mm gun and low silhouette made it an ideal vehicle for its role.

As with other successful vehicles there emerged a series of variations based on the M18. The Howitzer Motor Carriage T88 had a 105 mm howitzer but the project was cancelled. With the turret removed the vehicle became the Armoured Utility Vehicle M39 which was used for a variety of roles from APC to gun towing. There were also several amphibious trial vehicles, none of which saw service.

Data Gun Motor Carriage M18

Weight in action	18,160 kg/40,000 lb
Maximum road speed	Up to 88.5 kph/55 mph
Road range	241 km/150 miles
Length with gun	6,655 mm/262 inches
Length of hull	5,436 mm/214 inches
Width	2,972 mm/117 inches
Height	2,576.5 mm/101.44 inches
Width	2,870 mm/113 inches
Engine horse power	400
Track width	365.7 mm/14.4 inches
Wheel base	3,308 mm/130.25 inches
Armament	1 × 76 mm
	1 × .5-inch machine-gun
Ammunition carried	45 × 76 mm
	800 × .5-inch
Front armour	12.7 mm/0.5 inch
Side and rear armour	12.7 mm/0.5 inch
Turret front armour	25.4 mm/1 inch
Crew	5

five

American tank armament

When the USA entered the war in late 1941 nearly all tanks in front-line use mounted the 37 mm gun M6. This was a version of the M3 anti-tank gun, and differed from the earlier M5 in having a semi-automatic breech. When first produced the M6 was as good as any tank gun in service anywhere, but it was soon overtaken by the increases in gun calibre being introduced in Germany and elsewhere. Nevertheless, the 37 mm gun M6 was still in service as the war ended as the main armament of the Light Tanks M3 and M5 and was also used in the Light Tank (Airborne) M22.

To try and reach a parity with the German advances in calibre the American gun designers decided to plump for a 75 mm weapon to arm all future designs in the medium tank range. A new gun was designed and produced at the Watervliet Arsenal based on the old French Canon de 75 mle 1897. This gun had been in American service since 1918 when it was adopted as the standard American field gun. The first tank gun was the M2 which was followed by the M3 with a longer barrel — otherwise the two were identical. The 75 mm gun M3 became the armament of the great bulk of tanks produced in the USA up till 1944. The M3 was a relatively simple, sturdy gun that gave excellent service, but by 1944 it was superseded by the 76 mm Tank Gun M1.

The 76 mm gun had a calibre of 76.2 mm which was the same as the 3-inch Tank Gun M7. This weapon was originally developed from the 3-inch Anti-aircraft Gun M3 and was first fitted into the Heavy Tank M6. Thereafter it was used not in tanks but in tank destroyers, the main vehicle so fitted being the Gun Motor Carriage M10.

While the 3-inch Tank Gun M7 was an adaptation of an existing anti-aircraft gun, the 76 mm Tank Gun M1 was a weapon developed specifically for the tank role. There were three main versions: the M1 was the first version with no muzzle brake; the M1A1 had the trunnions moved to improve

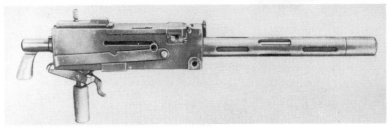

Machine-gun cal .30 inch.

balance, and the M1A2 was fitted with a muzzle brake. Numbers of M1A1s were also adapted to take a muzzle brake and these then became the M1A1C. The 76 mm M1 was a good, hard-hitting gun. It entered service in 1944 and became the standard gun for the late M4 series.

Good as the 76 mm gun was, the projected heavy tanks demanded a heavier weapon. Again an anti-aircraft barrel was adapted to the tank role, this time the starting point being the 90 mm Gun M1 which became the 90 mm Gun M3. The 90 mm Gun M3 was the main armament of the Heavy Tank M26 and was also used in the Gun Motor Carriage M36. Despite its parity in size with the famous German '88' it was not as powerful, but it was the most hard-hitting of all the American tank guns.

Although not strictly a tank gun mention must be made of the 105 mm Howitzer M4. This was fitted to the Medium Tank M4 and M4A3 in order to give heavy fire support to tank and infantry operations.

All the guns mentioned above were fitted with gyro-stabilisation, in elevation at least. The idea of gyro-stabilisation was to keep a gun pointed at its target even when the tank was lurching about on the move. Such a facility was a most valuable asset as a gun so fitted could be aimed and any subsequent rapid changes in elevation caused by the movement of the tank

would be 'damped out' so the gun barrel would still point at its target. But the asset was often wasted as tank gunners frequently preferred to fire from a standing position to make sure the target was hit first time.

Common equipment on nearly every type of American tank was the machine-gun calibre .30-inch M1919. Belt-fed and air-cooled, this machine-gun was used either as a co-axial weapon alongside the main armament, as a pintle-mounted AA gun, or as the bow machine-gun. The gun could be dismounted from any of these positions and mounted on a tripod for ground use. Ammunition was fed in 250 round fabric or metal link belts and cyclic rate of fire was 400-500 rounds per minute.

The other machine-gun used on many American tanks was the

Left *75mm guns M3 being installed in M4 Medium Tank turrets.* **Right** *M4 Gun Gyrostabilizer.*

American tank armament

Above *Machine-gun cal .30 inch on AA bracket mount on Light Tank M5.* **Right** *Machine-gun .50s on AA pintle mounts.*

machine-gun calibre .5-inch M2 which was an enlarged version of the M1919. Due to its size this machine-gun was usually mounted externally on an AA pintle on the turret, but could also be dismounted for use on a tripod. Rate of fire was 450-575 rounds per minute and ammunition was fed into this powerful weapon in 110-round metal link belts.

Gun data

	Calibre (mm)	Length overall (in)	Muzzle velocity (ft/sec) (max)	Shell weight (HE lb)	Shot weight (AP lb)	Armour penetration (mm/yards)
37 mm Gun M6	37	82.5	2,900	1.61	1.92	61 at 500
75 mm Gun M2	75	91.75	1,860	14.6	14.92	60 at 500
75 mm Gun M3	75	118.38	2,300	14.6	14.92	70 at 500
3-inch Gun M7	76.2	158.1	2,700	18	15.43	80 at 1,000
76 mm Gun M1	76.2	167.75	2,800	18	15.43	88 at 1,000
90 mm Gun M3	90	186.15	2,700	23.4	23.4	120 at 1,000
105 mm howitzer M4	105	98 (approx)	1,550	33	—	—

American Tanks of World War 2

six

Camouflage and markings

Basically, all vehicles belonging to the United States Army and Marine Corps, armoured or otherwise, were finished in a uniform dull medium green, sometimes described as olive drab. The exact shade varied according to the time between repaint jobs, the amount of exposure to sunlight and other elements, and inevitably the paint batch and how well it was stirred. This general application of olive green was in spite of carefully worked out 'official' specifications that covered every military item from tanks to rifles. These 'official schemes' involved the use of several paint shades, which varied from battle theatre to battle theatre, applied in 'jigsaw' fashion. Among the colours to be used were green, shades of brown, grey, white and sand. As far as is known these 'official' schemes were never used in service. Almost every vehicle was finished in olive drab and this was only altered to suit local conditions. When the need for a local scheme had passed the olive drab reappeared.

The first American tanks to see action were probably those of the US Marine Corps in the Pacific. These Light Tanks went into action in standard olive drab, although they were soon smeared in coral dust and sand, and festooned with palm fronds.

American tanks in North Africa originally appeared in strict olive drab, but as they moved into action in Tunisia, where the Luftwaffe had established local air supremacy, the need to merge more with the surrounding terrain resulted in wholesale improvisation using local earth and mud daubed over the basic finish. The earth/mud varied from rich brown through to pale grey depending upon the locality. Some artillery vehicles appeared in the summer of 1943 in what appears to have been olive drab over-painted in US Army engineer sand in aircraft-style patches but this may have been a 'one-off' scheme as it does not appear to have been applied elsewhere.

The best excursion into camouflage occurred in December 1944 during the Ardennes offensive. The Allies had enjoyed air supremacy all the way from Normandy, but with Hitler's desperate offensive bad weather grounded the Allied air forces. Thus it was tank versus tank in the snow and the Americans hastily hid their olive drab with every tin of white paint they could find. After a few weeks the Mustangs and Thunderbolts were back and the white finish was gone forever.

Although not strictly a camouflage finish, American tanks during the autumn of 1944 and after were often seen carrying extra extemporised armour to protect their relatively thin armour from the effects of the hollow-charge weapons such as the Panzerfaust and Panzerschreck used by German tank-killer squads. This extra 'armour' often took the form of sandbags or timber held in place on the tank sides, front and top with wire. The wood was sometimes uncut logs and sometimes thick baulks of timber. In extreme cases extra layers of concrete were added.

National markings

The basic US national marking when America entered the war was a white five-pointed star, painted in varying sizes and positions. This was altered slightly by a surrounding circle in 1943. By 1944 a stencilled version had been introduced which gave the effect of a broken circle.

The American national flag also appeared on AFVs, albeit briefly, during the 'Torch' landings in French North Africa. The red part of the stripes was frequently omitted.

Unit markings

The US Army used a simple and very legible code for identifying the 'owners' of their vehicles. Broken down it indicated division (and type), regiment or battalion (and type), followed separately but on the same level by the company letter vehicle number. Thus: 2 67 △ D3 indicated vehicle No 3, company D, 67th Armoured Regiment, 2nd Armoured Divison. The triangular symbol △ signified 'armoured'.

However, these markings vanished under the coats of olive drab in Tunisia, and were replaced, in the case of the US 1st Armoured Division, by a series of geometrical symbols. By late 1943 little evidence is left of any unit markings on AFVs, and they seem to have disappeared entirely on 'pure' armour from that time on. But they did appear on self-propelled guns of tank destroyer units in North-West Europe in 1944. Examples were: 1A634TD on an M10 of the 1st Armoured Division and 3A705TD B14 on an M18 of the 3rd Armoured Division. Note that by 1944 the triangular 'armour' symbol had been replaced by a plain 'A'.

Vehicle serial numbers

These appeared, mostly in orange-yellow but sometimes in white, on the hull sides. They consisted of a number preceded by the letters USA. Sometimes this number also appeared on the hull rear and front. The USA was sometimes omitted.

Appendix

Tank production totals

The period covered is from 1940 until December 31 1945

Producer	Total
Detroit Tank Arsenal	22,234
American Car & Foundry	15,224
Fisher Tank Arsenal, Grand Blanc	13,137
Cadillac Motor Company	10,142
Pressed Steel	8,648
Pullman-Standard	3,926
American Locomotive Works	2,985
Baldwin Locomotive Works	2,515
Massey Harris Company	2,473
Ford Motor Company	1,690
Lima Locomotive	1,655
Montreal Locomotive Works	1,144
Marmon-Herrington	1,070
Pacific Car and Foundry	926
Federal Machine	540
Rock Island Arsenal	94
International Harvester	7
Total	**88,410**

It is interesting to note that over the same period total British production was circa 24,800 and German production was of the order of 24,360.

American Tanks of World War 2